EASY PIANO

CLASSIC ROCK SHEET MUSIC HITS

Arranged by DAN COATES

Published 2004

© International Music Publications Ltd
Griffin House 161 Hammersmith Road London W6 8BS England

Editorial management: Artemis Music Limited (www.artemismusic.com)

After Midnight

Words and Music by J. J. Cale

Bad Moon Rising

Words and Music by John Fogerty

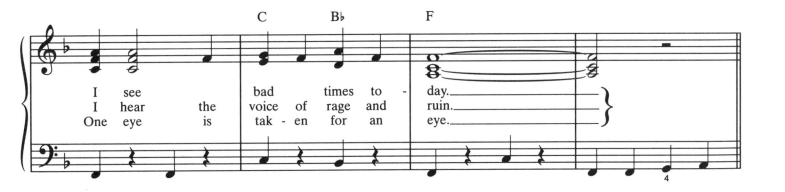

I see   bad   times to - day.____
I   hear the   voice of rage and ruin.____
One eye   is   tak - en for an eye.____

Don't go a-round to - night,__ well, it's bound to take your life.__

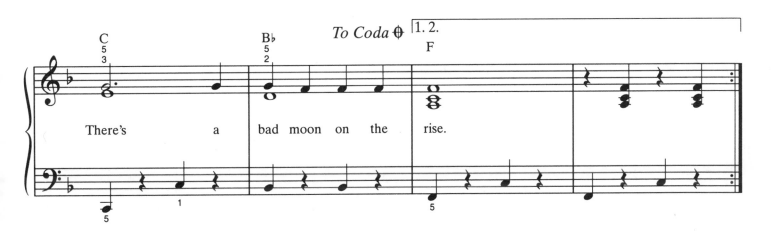

To Coda

There's   a   bad moon on the rise.

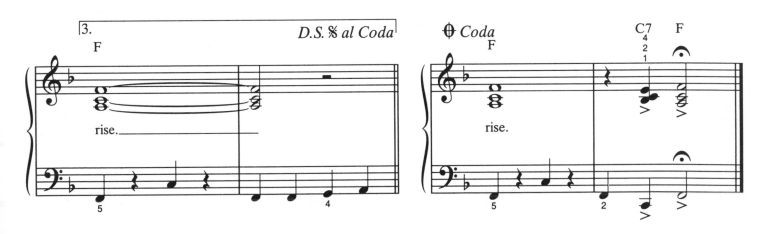

D.S. al Coda   *Coda*

rise.____   rise.

Black Water

Words and Music by Patrick Simmons

With a bright, steady beat

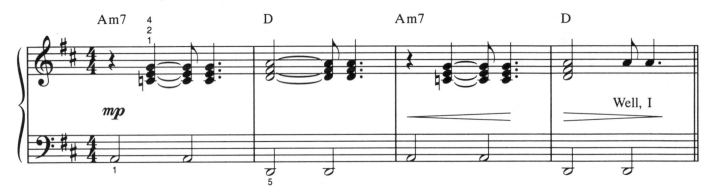

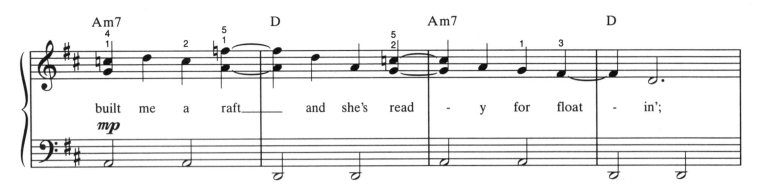

built me a raft____ and she's read - y for float - in';

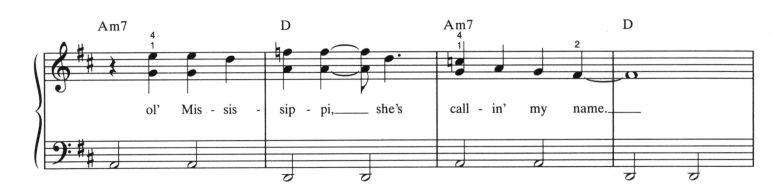

ol' Mis - sis - sip - pi,____ she's call - in' my name.____

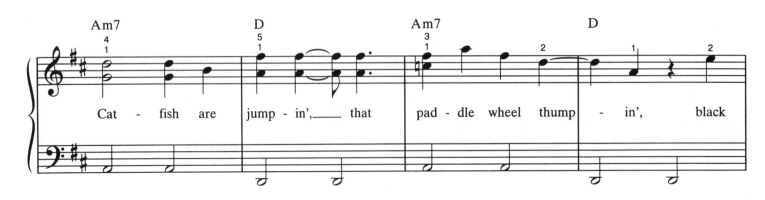

Cat - fish are jump - in',____ that pad - dle wheel thump - in', black

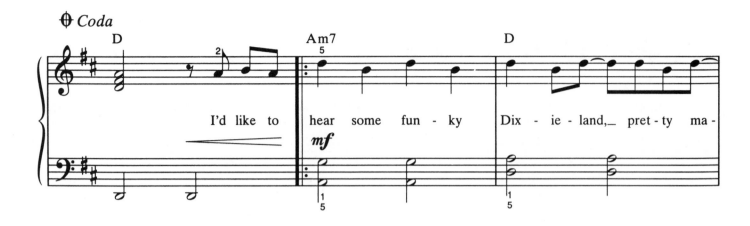

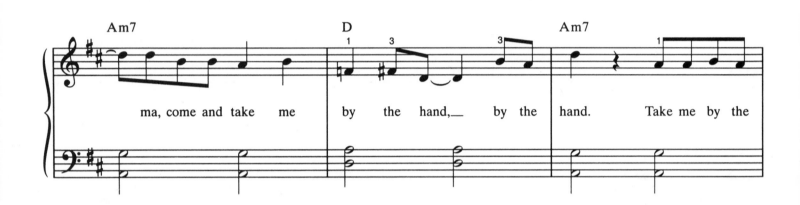

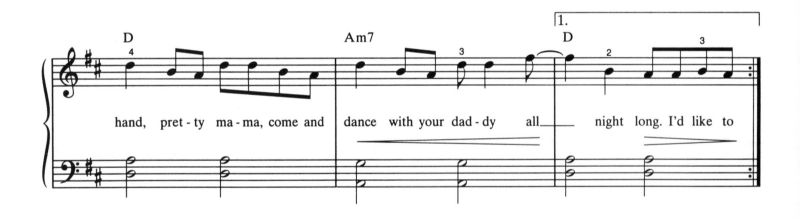

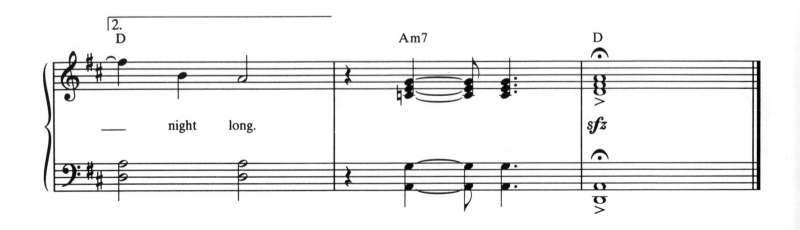

Desperado

Words and Music by Don Henley and Glenn Frey

Cat's In The Cradle

Words and Music by Harry Chapin and Sandy Chapin

15

16

To Coda

shook his head   and he | said with a smile,___ "What I'd | real - ly like, Dad, is to

bor - row the car___ keys. | See you lat - er. Can I | have them, please?"   And the

D.S. %̸ al Coda

Coda

then.

4. I've

Verse 4:

long   since re - tired,   my | son's moved a - way. | I called him up   just the

18

Don't Let The Sun Go Down On Me

Words by Bernie Taupin
Music by Elton John

Fro-zen here on the lad-der of my life.

Too late___ to save my-self from fall - ing.

I took a chance and changed your way of life.

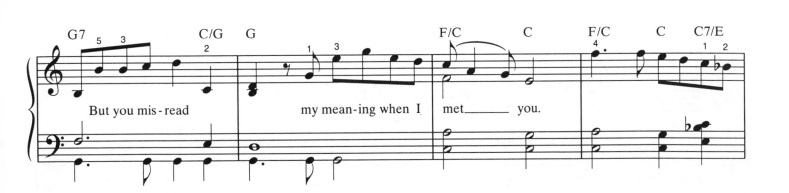

But you mis-read my mean-ing when I met___ you.

22

Down On The Corner

Words and Music by John Fogerty

Brightly, a la Calypso

1. Ear - ly in the eve - nin' just a - bout sup - per time,
2. Roos - ter hits the wash - board and peo - ple just got to smile,
3. You don't need a pen - ny just to hang a - round,

but o - ver by the court - house they're
if you've got a nick - el, won't you
Blink - y thumps the gut bass and

start - ing to un - wind.
so - los for a - while.
lay your mon - ey down?
Four kids on the cor
Poor - boy twangs the rhy
O - ver on the cor -

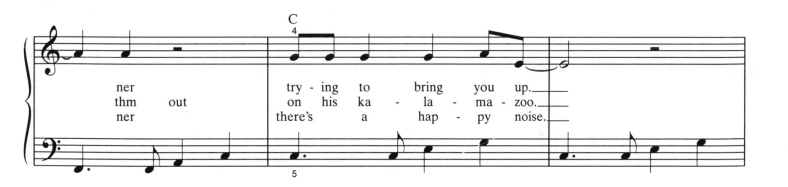

ner   try - ing to   bring   you   up.
thm out   on his ka - la - ma - zoo.
ner   there's a   hap - py   noise.

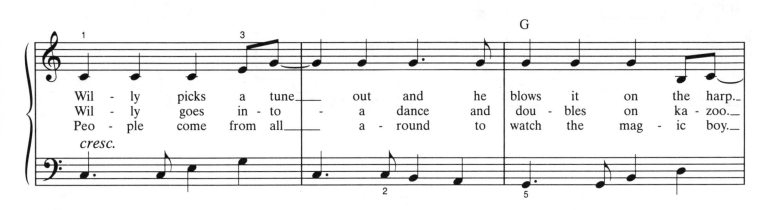

Wil - ly picks a tune   out and he blows it   on the harp.
Wil - ly goes in - to a dance and dou - bles on ka - zoo.
Peo - ple come from all a - round to watch the mag - ic boy.

cresc.

Down   on the cor -   ner,

f

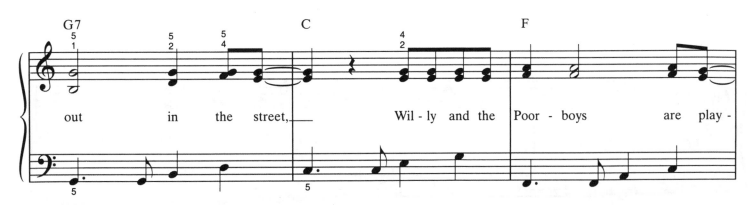

out   in the street,   Wil - ly and the Poor - boys   are play -

Down on the Corner - 3 - 2

Gimme Some Lovin'

Words and Music by Steve Winwood, Muff Winwood and Spencer Davis

Europa
(Earth's Cry Heaven's Smile)

Music by Carlos Santana and Tom Costa

Coda

Go Your Own Way

Words and Music by Lindsey Buckingham

Higher Love

Words and Music by Steve Winwood and Will Jennings

I'd Lie For You
(And That's The Truth)

Words and Music by Diane Warren

Moderately slow ♩ = 88

Verse:

1. I'd nev-er tell you one lie, ___ I'd nev-er let you down. I'd nev-er leave, I'd be the
2. Just take a look in my eyes, ___ you'll see a love that's blind. Just take a hold of my hand,

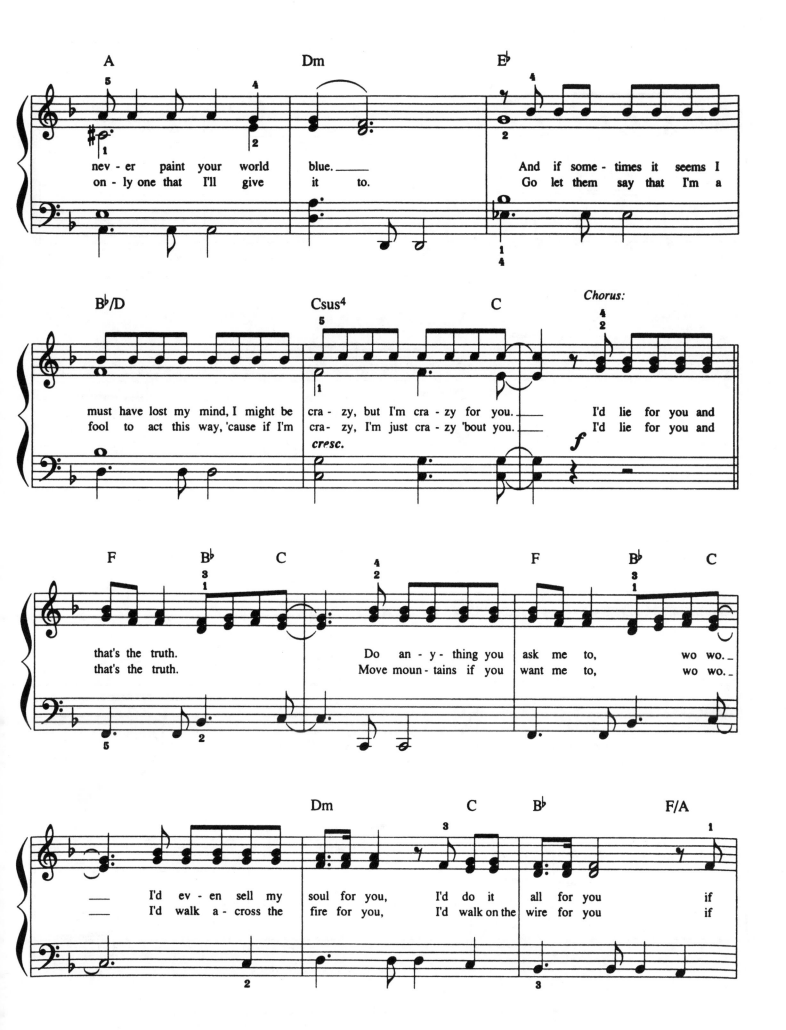

Hotel California

Words and Music by Don Henley, Glenn Frey and Don Felder

I Don't Want To Miss A Thing

Words and Music by Diane Warren

Layla

Words and Music by Jim Gordon and Eric Clapton

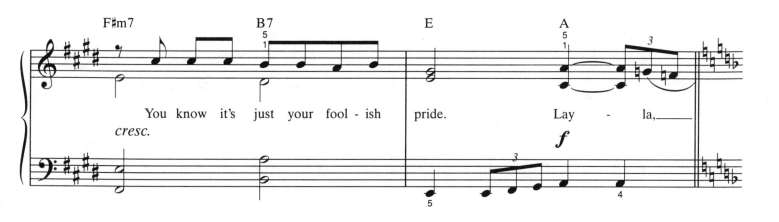

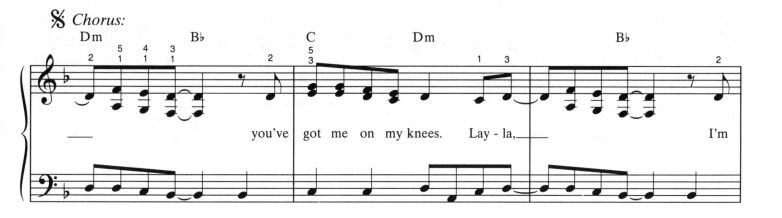

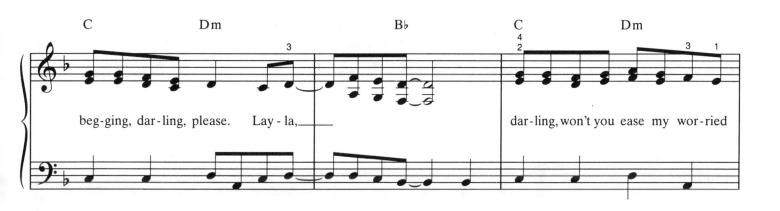

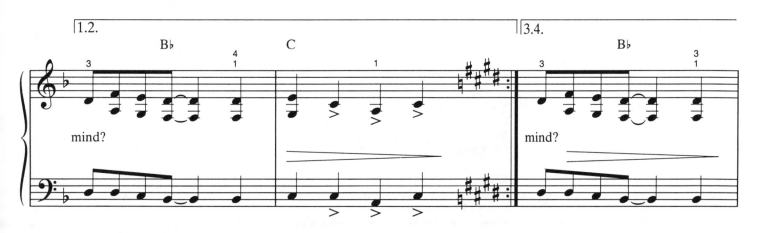

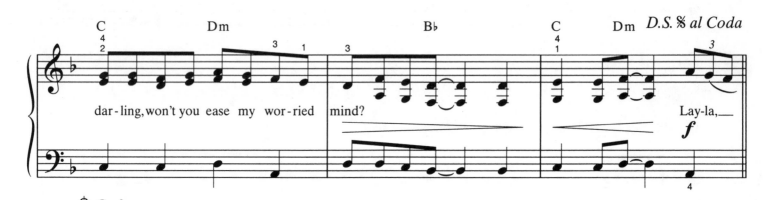

Verse 2:
Tried to give you consolation,
Your old man won't let you down.
Like a fool, I fell in love with you.
You turned my whole world upside down.
(To Chorus:)

Verse 3:
Make the best of the situation
Before I finally go insane.
Please don't say we'll never find a way
And tell me all my love's in vain.
(To Chorus:)

Lyin' Eyes

Words and Music by Don Henley and Glenn Frey

The Living Years

Lyrics by B.A. Robertson
Music by B.A. Robertson and Mike Rutherford

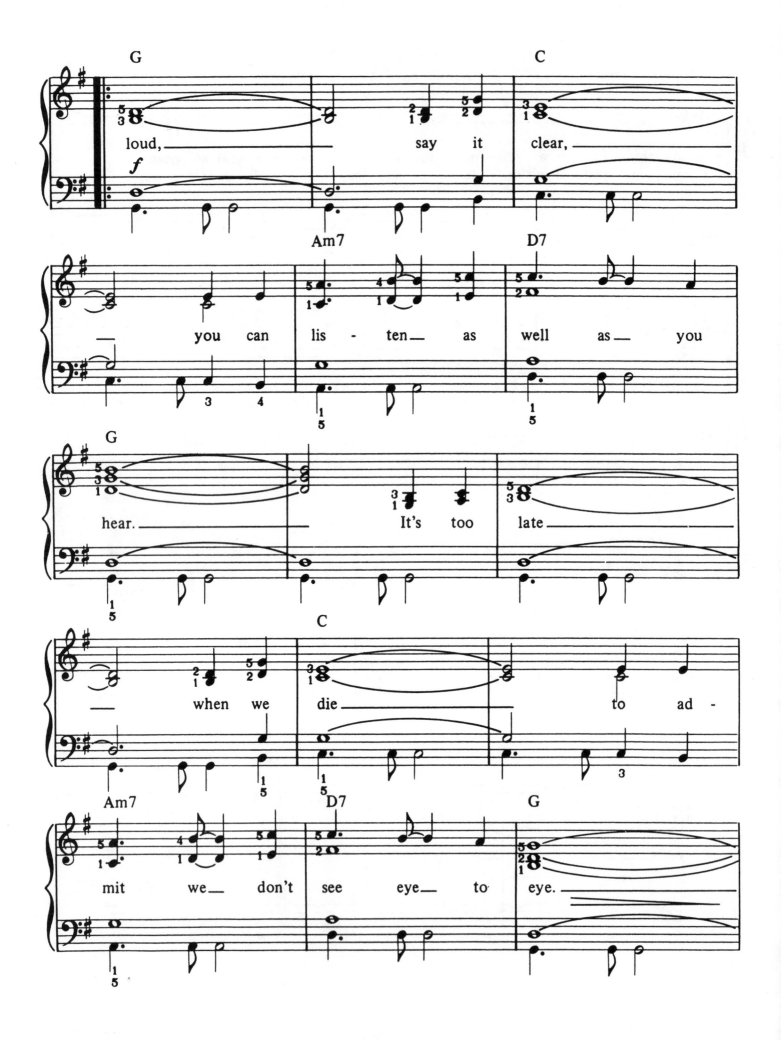

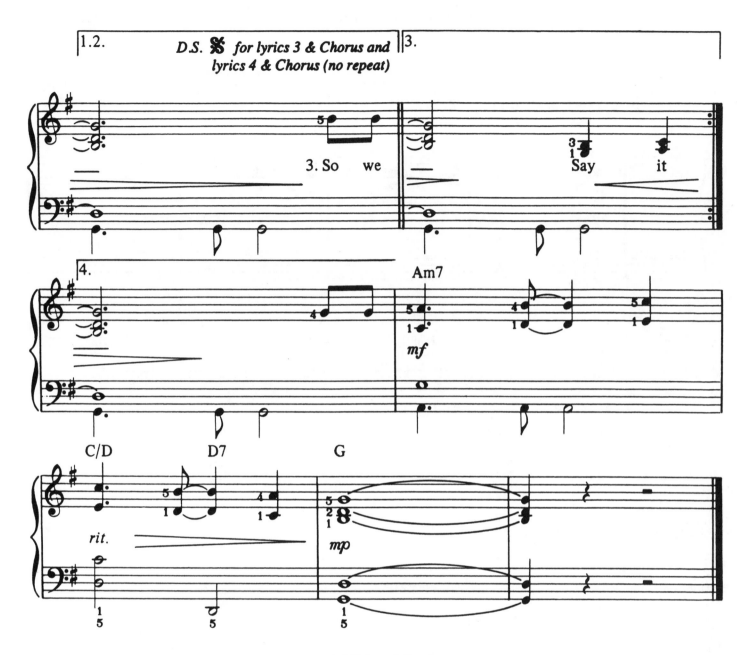

Additional Lyrics

3. So we open up a quarrel
   Between the present and the past.
   We only sacrifice the future,
   It's the bitterness that lasts.
   So don't yield to the fortunes
   You sometimes see as fate.
   It may have a new perspective
   On a different day.
   And if you don't give up, and don't give in
   You may just be O.K.

   Chorus:

4. I wasn't there that morning
   When my father passed away.
   I didn't get to tell him
   All the things I had to say.
   I think I caught his spirit
   Later that same year.
   I'm sure I heard his echo
   In my baby's new born tears.
   I just wish I could have told him
   In the living years.

   Chorus:

Long Train Runnin'

Words and Music by Tom Johnston

Maggie May

Words and Music by Rod Stewart and Martin Quittenton

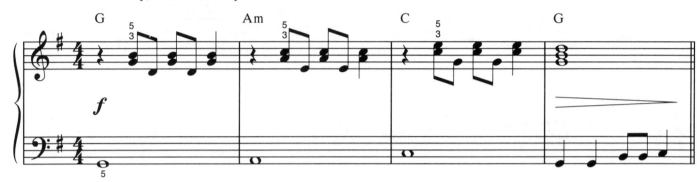

Wake up, Mag-gie, I think I got some-thing to say to you.___

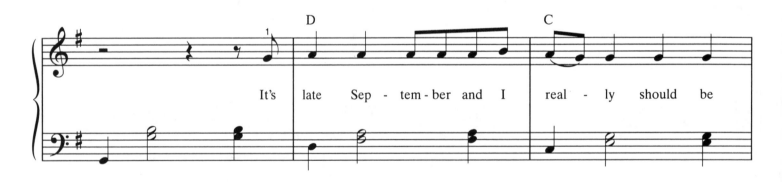

It's late Sep - tem-ber and I real - ly should be

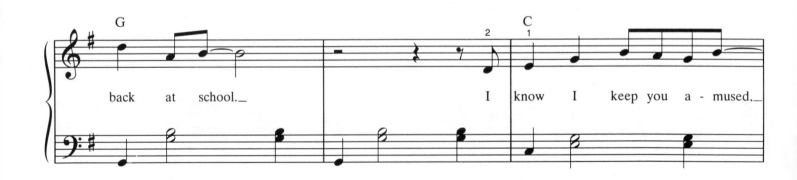

back at school.___ I know I keep you a - mused,___

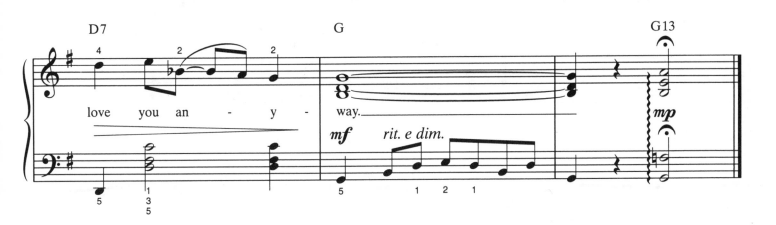

Verse 2:
You lured me away from home, just to save you from being alone.
You stole my soul, that's a pain I can do without.
All I needed was a friend to lend a guiding hand.
But you turned into a lover, and Mother, what a lover! You wore me out.
All you did was wreck my bed, and in the morning kick me in the head.
Oh, Maggie, I couldn't have tried anymore.

Verse 3:
You lured me away from home, 'cause you didn't want to be alone.
You stole my heart, I couldn't leave you if I tried.
I suppose I could collect my books and get back to school.
Or steal my Daddy's cue and make a living out of playin' pool,
Or find myself a rock and roll band that needs a helpin' hand.
Oh, Maggie, I wish I'd never seen your face.
(To Tag:)

More Than A Feeling

Words and Music by Tom Scholz

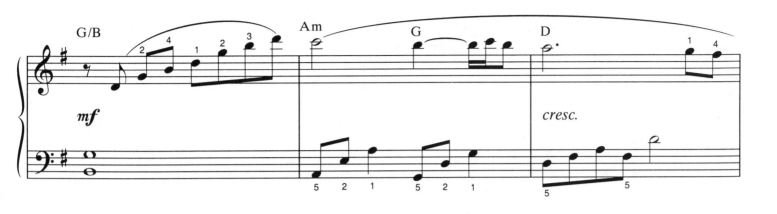

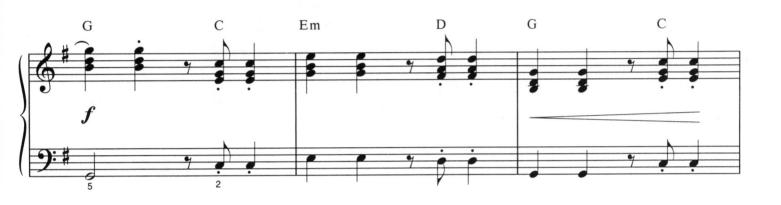

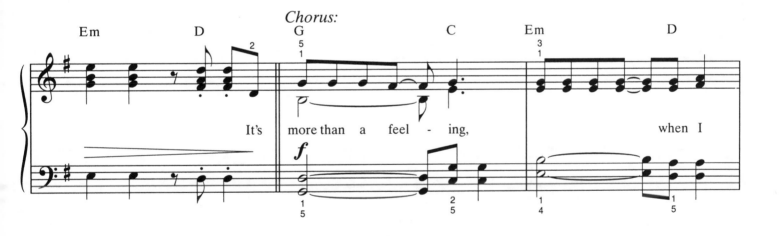

Chorus:

It's more than a feel - ing, when I

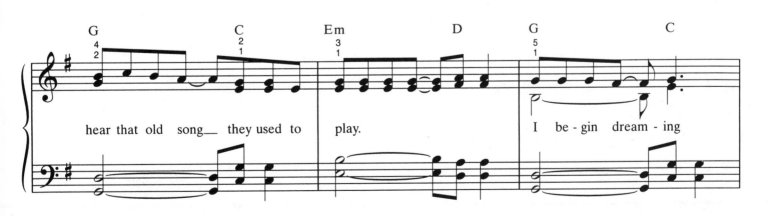

hear that old song__ they used to play. I be - gin dream - ing

Verse 3:
When I'm tired and thinking cold,
I hide in my music, forget the day
And dream of a girl I used to know.
I closed my eyes and she slipped away.
(To Chorus:)

Open Arms

Words and Music by Jonathan Cain and Stephen Perry

Proud Mary

Words and Music by John Fogerty

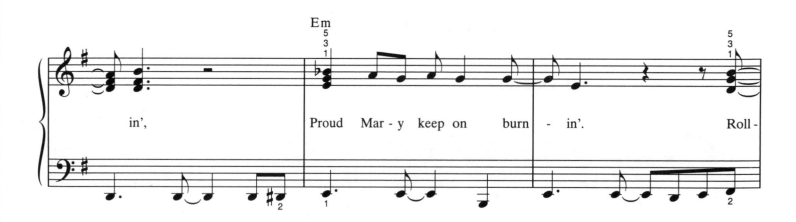

in', Proud Mar - y keep on burn - in'. Roll-

in', roll - in', roll - in' on the riv - er.___

Verse 3:

3. If you come down___ to the riv - er,

mf

bet you gon-na find some peo - ple who live.___ You don't have to wor - ry

Sister Golden Hair

Words and Music by Gerry Beckley

Something About The Way You Look Tonight

Words by Bernie Taupin
Music by Elton John

Moderately slow ♩ = 72

Sorry Seems To Be The Hardest Word

Words by Bernie Taupin
Music by Elton John

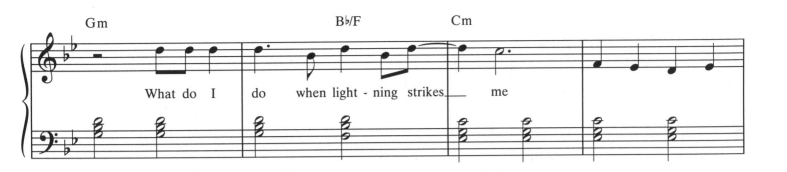

96

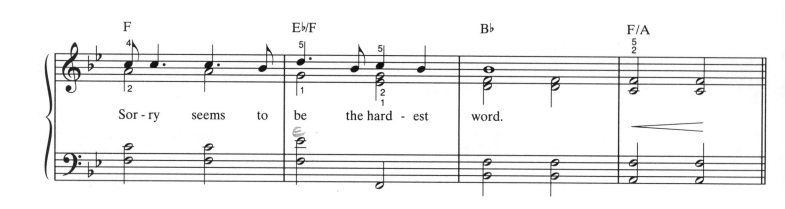

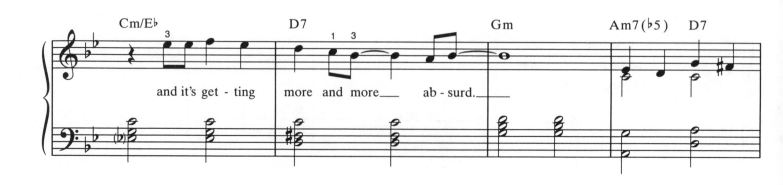

It's sad,_____ it's so sad._____ Why can't__ we talk____ it o - ver?_____

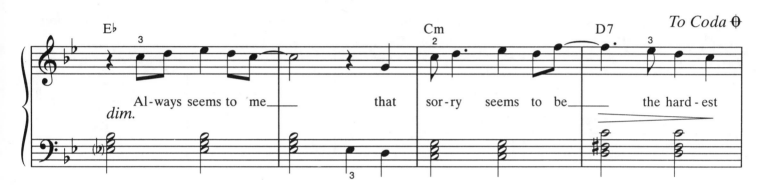

To Coda ⊕

Al-ways seems to me____ that sor-ry seems to be_____ the hard - est

dim.

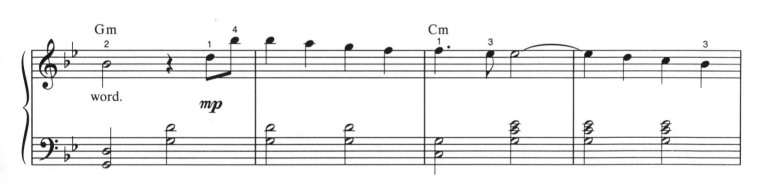

word.

mp

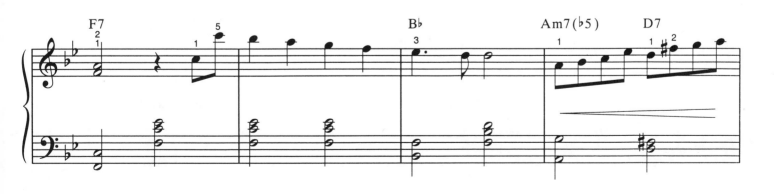

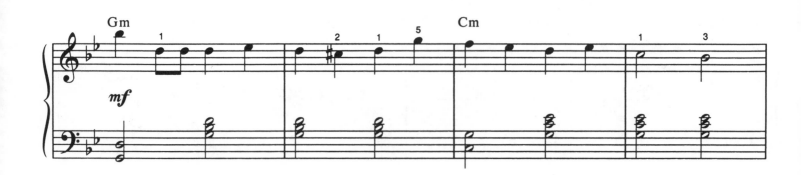

D.C. al Coda

⊕ Coda

word. What do I do to make you love____ me?

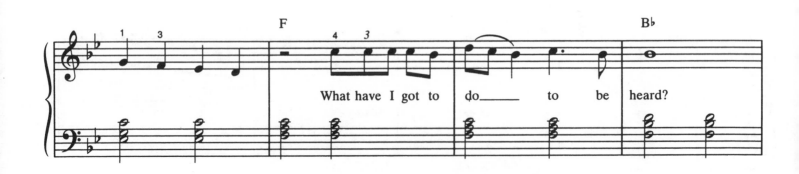

What have I got to do____ to be heard?

What A Fool Believes

Words and Music by Kenneth Loggins and Michael McDonald

With a bright, steady tempo

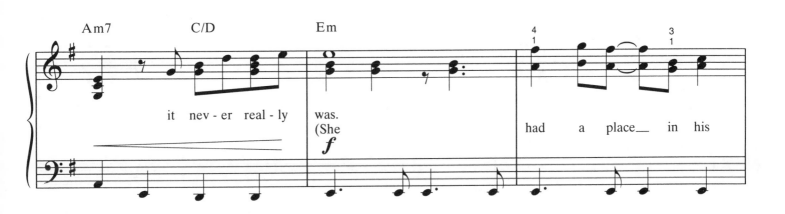

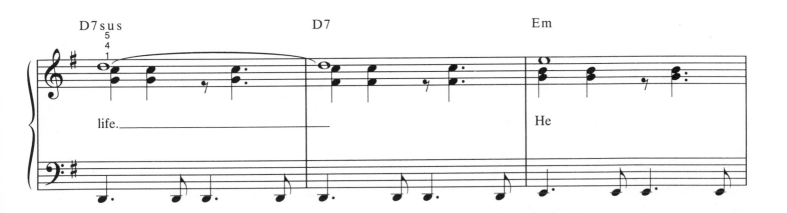

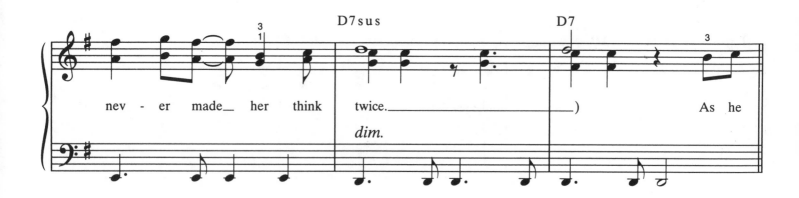

nev - er made__ her think twice._____) As he

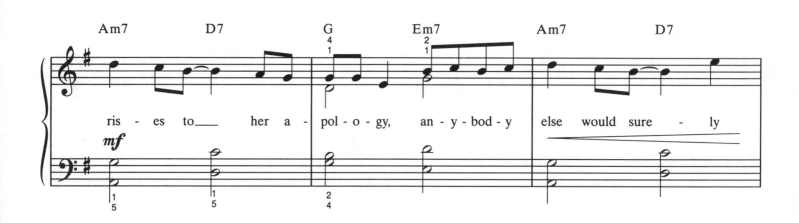

ris - es to__ her a - pol - o - gy, an - y - bod - y else would sure - ly

know he's watch - ing her go.

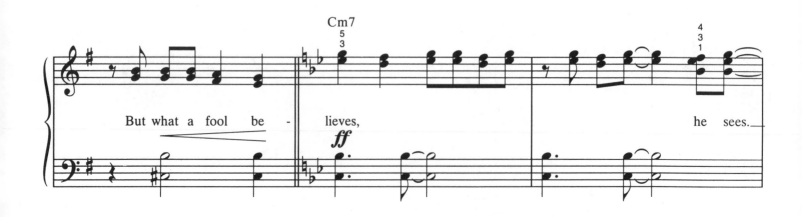

But what a fool be - lieves, he sees.__